The ACADEMY of BARMY COMPOSERS

Welcome to

BAROQUE

Mark Llewelyn Evans
Illustrations Karl Davies

GRAFFEG

How the heck did this book come about?

Was it because my mum, 'Liz the Lyric', decided to save a theatre? Or because I popped off to the Guildhall School of Music & Drama to train as an opera singer? Was it because in school I was never allowed to take English Literature as my spelling was too bad? I suppose the reasons could go on and on, but that would be boring...

I think it's down to my favourite, the amazing Myfi. Like most children, my daughter LOVED a bedtime story. I would be nagged: 'Daddy, I want one of your made up stories.' We cuddled up each night and left our small bedroom behind to go on adventures around the world, meeting fairies, heroes and kingdoms darker than dark, talking fish and lots more, as this went on for fifteen years – well, almost!

Thanks, Myfi, for listening to my stories and for telling me to keep going. Thanks, Mum and Dad, for taking me to the theatre, where all children should discover great adventures, and to all the young people that I have met through the ABC of Opera who have inspired me to use spell-check and tell this almost-real story.

Mark Llewelyn Evans

ABC of Opera, The Academy of Barmy Composers: Baroque.
Published in Great Britain in 2019 by Graffeg Limited.

Written by Mark Llewelyn Evans copyright © 2019. Illustrated by Karl Davies copyright © 2019. Additional material by Lorraine King.
Designed and produced by Graffeg Limited copyright © 2019.

Graffeg Limited, 24 Stradey Park Business Centre, Mwrwg Road, Llangennech, Llanelli, Carmarthenshire SA14 8YP Wales UK Tel 01554 824000 www.graffeg.com

Mark Llewelyn Evans and Karl Davies are hereby identified as the authors of this work in accordance with section 77 of the Copyrights, Designs and Patents Act 1988.

A CIP Catalogue record for this book is available from the British Library.

ISBN 9781912213863

1 2 3 4 5 6 7 8 9

CONTENTS

CHAPTER 1
The Mystery of the Music Hall

Across the bridge and up the winding road that climbs high above the village of **Pontirgorffennol** stands a sad, boarded-up music hall. It once filled the hearts of the villagers with joy and laughter, but these days only the wind rattles and stirs the eerie old building. Best friends **Jack** and **Megan** were determined to discover its mysteries. They approached and peered through the rusty, spiky gates. There was no going back now.

'Megan, are you crazy? This is a terrible idea. Let's go home,' urged Jack.

'Jack, come on, don't be such a **SCAREDY** CAT!' Megan said, tugging at his sleeve.

'But what if there are ghosts inside...?' Jack asked.

'BOO!' shouted Megan.

'Megan! **STOP IT!**' cried Jack.

'Come on. Your gran says it's over **150** years old and full of stories and treasure – let's investigate!'

'Gran's 150 years old more like!' said Jack.

And so, with curiosity egging them on, the children climbed over the rickety gate, tiptoed up to the imposing but fragile front door and pushed it open with a loud **squeal.**

They tentatively stepped inside, their hearts pounding like large timpani drums, BOOM...**BOOM**...**BOOM!**

Pontirgorffennol (pont i'r gorffennol) – a Welsh word that means 'bridge to the past'.

'This is soooooo spooky,' said Megan, stepping into the shadowy half-light of the building.

'Too spooky for me, I'm going!'

Jack turned to leave, but his foot found a loose, rotten floorboard.

'Woahh... HEEELLP!!'

Megan reached out to save her **BFF**, but it was too late. **Whoosh! Down, down, down** they fell, waking Trunk, the music hall's only resident. Surely they would break an arm, a leg or bruise a toe at least, but what happened was astonishing. Almost as if he had been expecting them, Trunk opened his lid to catch the pair who tumbled in.

'Jack, are you all right?' asked Megan.

'I think so...' answered Jack, in a daze.

'AH HA... AT LAST! HUMANS!'

'Who said that?' whispered Megan.

'IT'S A ^{G}HOSSS$_S$T^T^{T}T...' shuddered Jack.

'I was beginning to believe I'd been forgotten forever, but then I opened my lid when I heard you calling for **HEEEEEELLPP!'**

The children looked at each other, then down at the trunk.

'The... the... trunk, it's talking!' said Megan, **flabbergasted.**

'Talking?' interrupted Trunk. 'In fact, I speak **43** languages... My favourite is **Chamicuro**, only **8** of us left now, sadly. I've been waiting for someone to rescue me. And it's you two!'

Chamicuro – The Chamicuros are a native people from Peru in South America. Their language is one of the most endangered in the world.

The children couldn't believe what was happening.

'Let me explain,' Trunk continued. **'40** years ago, at the end of the last performance in this music hall, I was accidently locked away down here in the basement. Since then, I've been alone. Such a long wait... Well, never mind all that, you're here now and we've no time to waste! Not even a **hemidemisemiquaver** – we need to travel at **superluminal** speed!'

> A hemidemisemiquaver is traditionally the shortest musical note, a 64th, and looks like this. It's the fastest musical note in the world... Blink and you will miss it.

To the children's astonishment, Trunk appeared to fire up a pair of engines beneath him, and with a mighty **HUFF** and **PUFF** and what sounded like a **LARGE FART,** 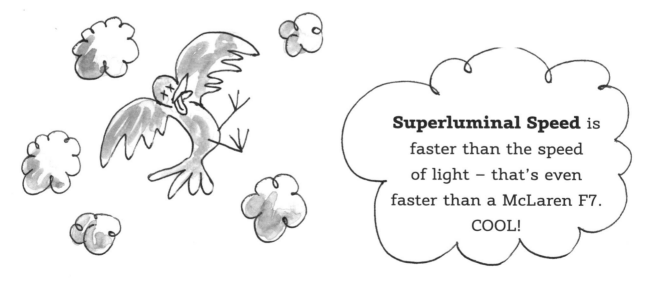 he propelled himself up through the broken floorboards, out of the open door and into the starlit sky with his rescuers hanging on for dear life.

'I'm all **discombobulated,** it's been so long since I flew. Where are my headlights?' Trunk yawned, narrowly missing a passing bird.

> **Superluminal Speed** is faster than the speed of light – that's even faster than a McLaren F7. COOL!

'Put us down now, Trunk!' Megan shouted.

'No time, sorry, I have to get home.'

'Home?' Jack asked worryingly.

'We live down there, and we've got school in the morning,' insisted Megan. 'Plus we don't have passports.'

Trunk laughed. 'No passport needed – we are off to the land of **pasta and pizza.**'

'Where?' asked Jack.

'The country shaped like a boot, where I was made!' Trunk said.

'ITALY!' squealed Megan.

'Yes, and where we'll find the ABC!' said Trunk.

'The ABC?' questioned the children.

'The ABC of Opera, of course!
Now buckle up,' said Trunk.
Two seatbelts flew over the
children's shoulders, **Clunk! Click!**
and Trunk burst into song:

'Where did it all begin, the stories and the glories of the
opera? **The ABC, the ABC, the ABC of Opera!**'

CHAPTER 2
The Academy

In no time at all, the new friends were hovering in the warm Florentine air and ready to take their final turn.

'I can smell pizza,' Jack shouted. **'I LOVE PIZZA!'**

'Welcome to Italy, my friends. Hold tight, I'm a total disaster when it comes to landings!' Trunk shouted.

BASH! Crunch! OUCH! Splat!

Jack and Megan tumbled out and hit the ground with a **THUD**, followed by Trunk, who crashed into a cypress tree.

'Oh, sorry about that, *amici*. Not one of my better efforts, I'll admit,' he said, embarrassed.

'Don't worry, nothing's broken,' said Jack, putting Trunk at ease.

The children got to their feet, feeling dazed and a little bit **topsy-turvy**, and spotted a tall, odd-looking gentleman rushing towards them. He had long golden curls, wore colourful tights, a pair of shorts that looked like a filled nappy, and the biggest smile they had ever seen. Trunk shook himself off and introduced the new arrivals to the golden-haired gent.

Amici – 'friends' in Italian.

'*Ciao, ragazzi.* Welcome to **Baroque**, the home of the Baa-rockers. I'm **Professor Peri**, the **INVENTOR of Opera**. I heard that terrible landing from the Academy. I'd recognise it anywhere!'

'Academy?' chorused Jack and Megan.

'Why, the **ABC** of course, The Academy of Barmy Composers! Don't tell me you've never heard of us?'

'Well, Trunk did mention something,' said Megan.

'Where the 'eck have you been?' Peri snapped, turning to Trunk. 'Forrrrrrty years we 'ave waited for your return. Not a phone call, not a postcard, nothing!'

'I thought I had been forgotten,' Trunk replied.

'Forgotten? Never!' said Peri.

'Where exactly are we?' asked Jack.

'Why, we are in Florence, Italy,' replied Peri, 'it's **1597.**'

'Is that before dinosaurs?' interrupted Megan.

'Ha, no...' laughed Peri.

'Are you in fancy dress? Is that really your hair?' she asked.

'My nickname is **Golden Locks.**'

'Goldilocks? That's a girl's name,' sniggered Jack.

Peri laughed. 'Eh? No, GOLDEN locks! Now, no more questions... **BASTA!**'

Peri waved his hands very theatrically, took a deep breath and sang, **'A, B, C.'** Everything seemed to shake as a great golden palace emerged from the ground. The magnificent doors swung open, revealing swanky velvet drapes, sparkling crystal chandeliers and lavishly painted walls. The lights from a thousand candles flickered, and an enchanting, unfamiliar music flooded out to greet the children.

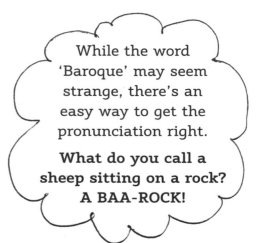

While the word 'Baroque' may seem strange, there's an easy way to get the pronunciation right.

What do you call a sheep sitting on a rock? A BAA-ROCK!

Ciao – 'hello' or 'goodbye' in Italian.
Ragazzi – 'children' in Italian.
Basta – 'that's enough' in Italian.

'Welcome to **The Academy of Barmy Composers,** the ABC of Opera,' said Peri.

CHAPTER 3

The Stories and the Glories

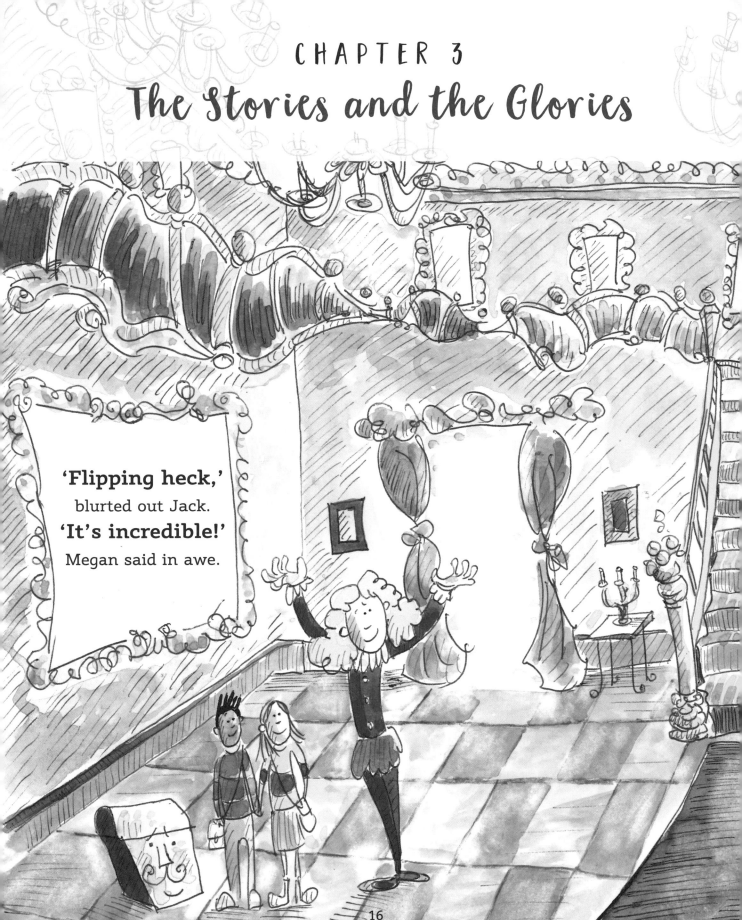

'Flipping heck,' blurted out Jack. 'It's incredible!' Megan said in awe.

From each corner of the breathtaking hall rushed the **Baa-rockers** to greet the new guests.

'We're composers and we are quirky, QUIRKY
We love to have fun and to party, PARTY
We write songs with plots, we are known as BAA-ROCKS,
We are Florence's cool "arty fartys"! FARTY'

'Ha, ha, **grazie,** my barmy **Baa-rockers**. Here we **compose** the best music ever!' Peri said. 'I invented opera, thanks to **Count Giovanni de' Bardi,** but all my operas seem to be lost.'

'That's a bit careless, I hate losing things,' said Megan.

'You're like my gran, she loses things all the time,' chipped in Jack.

'Well, being **500** years old has its challenges,' said the professore.

'Even Gran's not 500!' said Jack.

'So, what is opera?' Megan asked.

'And what's composing?' asked Jack.

'Composing is writing music, and a composer is the person who writes it,' Trunk said.

> **Count Giovanni de' Bardi (1534-1612)** was indeed a count, but unlike Count Dracula, he didn't bite. He was a nobleman and a soldier who loved music, reading and knowledge, especially tales from Ancient Greece – so the count invited lots of clever people around to his palace to invent stuff like OPERA.

> Professor Peri's first opera, *Dafne,* has been lost over the years...
> **DAFNE, WHERE ARE YOU?**
> **'Wherefore art thou, Dafne?'**

Grazie – 'thank you' in Italian.

19

'*Opera* is an Italian word meaning "*work*",' explained Peri.

'I hate work...so I'll hate **opera** too,' mumbled Jack.

'Don't worry, it's not like **algebra (93=180-z)**,' Peri went on. 'Opera is where amazing stories are brought to life with beautiful music.'

Jack smiled. 'Oh, cool! I love stories and music!' he said, beginning to warm to the crazy place.

'So do I!' added Megan.

'Opera can be **s i l l y**, **sad**, **scary** and *soppy*,' the professore continued.

'Soppy? Like kissing?! Yuk!' Jack looked like he was about to be sick.

'And the stories have knights, princesses, fairies and magic,' Trunk added.

'ABRACADABRA,' giggled Jack.

'And you invented it?' Megan asked.

'*Sì, sì*,' glowed Peri.

'So is it like **Pop** or **Hip-Hop**?' asked Jack.

'What about **R&B**? Or **Rap**?' Megan said, feeling sure she had it right.

Peri just shrugged his shoulders.

'I know, **Rock! Grime? Or Grunge?**'

Jack was running out of ideas.

Sì – 'yes' in Italian.

Opera has everything!

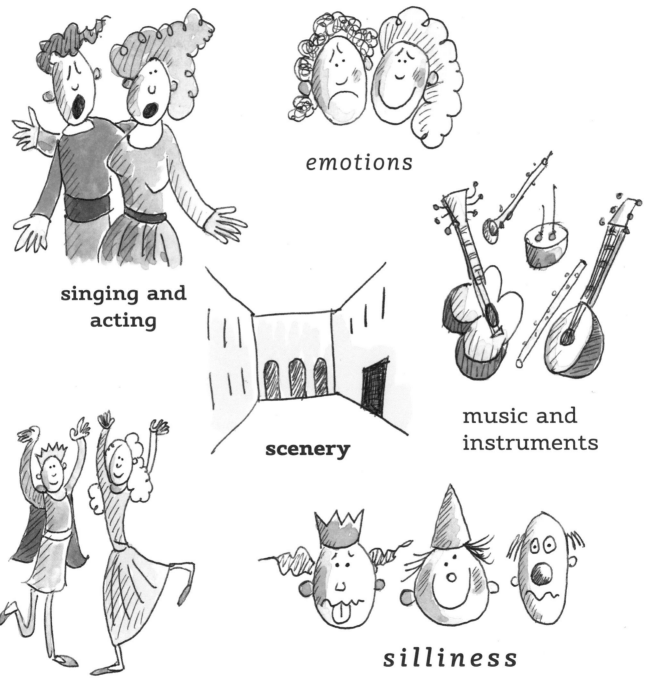

singing and acting

emotions

scenery

music and instruments

costumes and dancing

silliness

CHAPTER 4
Maestro Monte

'*Psst*,' Trunk hissed. Trunk had been trying to get Peri's attention for some time.

'What is it, Trunk?' Peri asked.

'In the future, opera has almost disappeared. It could soon be lost all together,' Trunk explained sadly.

Professor Peri looked worried. 'Not to **the FORGOTTEN LAND?**'

'Yes! We need help to keep opera alive, boss.'

'Is it really that bad, Trunk? Perhaps Jack and Megan could help us take opera back to the future?'

'I think they just might be the ones,' Trunk replied. 'They could stop opera being flushed down the loo like a poo.'

Before Peri could tell Trunk off, a horse came thundering towards the entrance door, skidding to a halt with great **AGITATO.** Its menacing rider was dressed head to toe in black, sporting a pointy beard topped off with a curly moustache. He jumped down from his steed and headed straight through the Academy's doors towards the professore.

'Liar, liar, liar, your pants are on fire. Opera is **MIA!'**

Agitato – Italian for 'in an agitated manner'. It is also used as an instruction for how a musician should play.
Mia – 'mine' in Italian.

'I am Claudio Monteverdi,
And I'm part of this musical journey,
Although Peri invented the opera,
I was first to make opera pop'lar.
Greek stories inspired me greatly,
So I dressed up my music ornately,
There was drama in all of my operas,
I was first to make opera pop'lar!'

'Your operas are lost, *stupido!*' said the incensed Monteverdi. 'I wrote the first **GREAT** opera, and I made it pop'lar.'

Professor Peri smiled nervously at the children. 'Don't worry, we get carried away. Opera is so **appassionata.**'

Before you could say *antipasti*, Maestro Monte pulled a salami from his cloak and **WHACKED** Peri on the head.

'Attacca! Attacca!

Fight me!' Monte said.
'I challenge you to a duel!'
    The children stood motionless.
Neither knew what to do.
Luckily, there was someone
who did...

Both Professor Peri
and Maestro Monte
wrote an opera about
the Greek tragedy
Orpheus. Read all
about it on page 65.

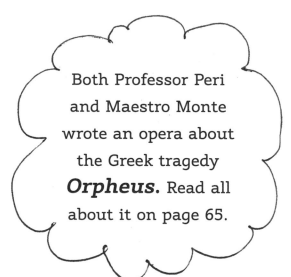

Stupido – 'stupid' in Italian.
Appassionata – 'passionate' in Italian.
Antipasti – 'snacks' or 'starters' in Italian.
Attacca – 'attack' in Italian and also a musical instruction used to indicate that the next section should follow without a pause.

CHAPTER 5
Fantastica Francesca

'BOYS! RAGAZZI! Stop! Maestro Monte, of course you are the Papà of opera, and Professor Peri, you are the inventor of opera... You are both *fantastici*!'

'Blimey, who is that?' Jack asked.

'She is sooooo cooooool,' gasped Megan.

Peri and Monte stopped in their tracks and looked adoringly at the *bella donna*, salamis akimbo.

'Ah, another girl! Who are you?' asked the new arrival.

'I'm Megan,' she answered excitedly.

'And *io sono* Fantastica Francesca Caccini, the first female opera composer.'

*'I'm a talented girl
Who can dance and sing,
The first prima donna to do... everything!
I dance, play the lute, and even guitar,
A composer as well, yes, a true superstar.
The first ever woman to write opera, too,
So, I guess you're now wondering,
What can't I do?'*

Fantastici – Italian for 'fantastic'.
Bella donna – 'beautiful lady' in Italian.
Prima donna – 'first lady' in Italian
and the leading female role in an opera.

Francesca flicked her hair and continued to tell the children her story.

'Papà was so proud of me for being a composer. In one of my operas, I had a good witch and a bad witch.'

'Like **The Wizard of Oz?**' said Megan.

'**Sì,**' smiled Francesca.

'That's **wicked**,' laughed Jack.

'**Scusi,** Francesca,' Peri interrupted. 'I must take the children to see more of **the Academy**, time is running out.'

'We could stay here all day!' said Jack.

'We are in no rush, Professore,' added Megan.

'No...but I think *we* might be,' commented Peri under his breath...

'See you later, Francesca, for a **cappuccino** or a **vino**.' Peri ushered the children along.

Music was already in Francesca's DNA, because her father, **Giulio Caccini (1551-1618)**, was one of the influential founders of opera. Like father like daughter, eh?

Francesca's nickname was *La Cecchina,* which means the song bird.

Scusi – 'excuse me' in Italian. *Cappuccino* – Frothy Italian coffee.
Vino – 'wine' in Italian. You can have red, white or
pink wine – like opera, it's made all over the world.

CHAPTER 6
It's All Over the World

'So, do *all* opera composers come from Italy?' asked Jack.

'Absolutely not,' Peri answered. 'You see, after opera left us here, it started popping up all over the place; **France, England, Germany, Russia, Austria,** and loads more countries! Kings, queens, lords, ladies, in fact, everyone wanted to see and hear opera.'

'Professore, you say opera has been around for 500 years, but haven't stories been around forever?' said Megan.

'Good point, my clever one. Yes, stories have been told since humans first walked the earth and people have sung songs from the beginning of time. What is different about my little invention, opera, is that you can act, sing and dance at the same time. *Magnifico!* Opera soon spread across the world.'

England – Every day, the British drink 165 million cups of tea. More languages (300) are spoken in London, the capital city, than in any other country in the world.

France – The capital city is Paris. The Eiffel Tower is 11,800 inches tall, or 324 meters tall.

Magnifico – 'magnificent' in Italian.

28

Germany – Makes some of the world's most amazing cars, including Audi, BMW and Porsche, as well as the most expensive car in the world, the Maybach Exelero. It is sheer perfection in every way and presently costs an overwhelming £6 million.

Russia – It's 6.612 million square miles, making it the largest country in the world. It is located across 9 time zones.

Austria – Vienna is the capital city of Austria. The Alps have some of the best skiing slopes in the world.

Italy – Italians invented pizza and ice cream. Nicknamed *Bel paese*, meaning 'beautiful country'.

CHAPTER 7
Doc Blow and Perfect Purcell

'Ah, perfect timing – *amici*, let me introduce you to two English opera composers,' Peri said.

Two gentlemen were walking towards them, both wearing wigs that looked like overweight sheep stuck on their heads (well, it is the Baa-rock period after all).

'**Scusate, signori,** you must meet Jack and Megan – they are from the future! **Ragazzi**, this is **Doc Blow** and **Perfect Purcell,** from **London.**'

The gentlemen bowed and waved their white lace handkerchiefs.

'How perfectly perfect to meet you, my dears,' said the London duo, bursting into perfect harmony.

'We both wrote operas,
We taught kings and queens,
At Westminster Abbey,
We made our fans scream!

Blow taught me music,
I'm the greatest, they say,
I leapt over my master,
And blew him away!

I agree, dear Purcell,
You were surging ahead,
But you ate too much chocolate,
And ended up dead!'

Scusate – 'excuse me' in Italian (plural).
Signori – Italian for 'mister' (plural).

Jack put his hand up. 'Excuse me, Mr Perfect Purcell, did you really die from eating too much chocolate...?'

'That's one theory, dear boy. Thanks to the Doc for reminding me,' said Purcell.

'Oh...what a way to go,' thought Jack, who loved his chocolate.

> The name **Purcell** comes from the old Norman French word *pourcel*, which means 'PIGLET'. *Oink, oink.*

Megan was more interested in Doc Blow, as she was desperate to discover how a pupil could eventually outsmart their teacher.

'Dr Blow, can pupils really be cleverer than their teachers?' she asked.

Doc Blow replied, 'Yes, teachers should help their students to be even better than they are, and that's what happened to the **FABULOUS** Purcell. Everyone loved him, especially the **Queen**.'

'I wonder if I could ever be better at science than my teacher, **Dr Bunsenburner**?' Jack said.

'Work hard and you just might!' Doc Blow said, as he released a giant

AAAAAAAAAAAHHHHHH-CHOOOOOOOOO!!,

throwing the children backwards into Trunk.

'**EXCUSE ME!**' interrupted a startled Trunk, shaking himself off.

'Come on gang,' urged Peri. 'I want you to meet more barmies.'
Peri waved his hands to beckon the children on.

'*Toodle pip,* **ACHOO!**' sneezed Doc Blow.

'Where to now?' asked Jack excitedly, brushing himself down.

'To the land of Frankfurters, castles and beer!'

'**GERMANY,**' Megan answered.

'Of course,' smiled the Prof.

Queen Mary II of England was a Stuart, the daughter of King James II (the last catholic monarch in Britain) and Purcell was her favourite composer. He wrote *Celebrate this Festival* for her birthday in 1693 and, sadly, her funeral music the following year.

CHAPTER 8
Too Hot to Handel

'Hallo,' said a gentleman with an even longer curly wig than the London duo. He had a very round belly and a terribly sad face, where the corners of his mouth drooped right down to the bottom of his chin. His heavy accent echoed as he sang:

'I am Herr Handel and I am a star,
Ven I vas a child, I dreamed I'd go far,
I wrote over 40 operas and oh, so much more,
Then I moved to London, the best place, for sure.
I became a Director of Music,
Ya, das is true,
At the Royal Academy, my repertoire grew.'

'Ja, I vas born in Germany, but I am now English,' Handel continued. 'Vhy, I even wrote music for the Royal Fireworks in **1749**. Mind you, it vas hard to hear my music above all ze explosions.'

Handel's dad was 63 when Handel was born in 1685 – the stars must have been perfectly aligned, as another two famous composers, Johan Sebastian Bach and Domenico Scarlatti, were born in the same year. (Read a little bit about them on page 62.)

Hallo – 'hello' in German (you'd never guess).
Herr – German for 'mister'.
Ja – 'yes' in German.

'**Coool,** I love fireworks!' Jack delighted in telling Herr Handel.

'It vasn't just the **fireworks** that ver noisy. The audiences ver so badly behaved, talking and shouting during my operas. And, can you believe it, the Queen came to see my opera and she broke ze chair, causing quite a calamity... It vas her big bum, not my opera's fault!

No vonder my vig turned vhite... Vorry, everything vas a vorry to me, I had so much vork, but it vas in Hamburg that I first became really famous.'

Handel's career was almost tragically cut short after a duel with fellow composer Johann Mattheson. The fierce quarrel between the two led Mattheson to almost kill Handel with his sword; fortunately, the blade caught Handel's jacket button, narrowly missing his heart.

CHAPTER 9
Luckless Lully

Suddenly, Peri and the children heard crashing, banging and shouting in yet another language coming towards them. A disaster was heading their way...

Tables, chairs and ornaments flew in every direction as the newcomer rushed in, waving his two crutches high in the air.

CRASH! BANG! 'MON DIEU!'

'Oh no... **Monsieur Luckless Lully,**' groaned Peri.

'**Quel désastre!**' Lully wiped his face with an already dripping hanky before noticing the children.

'Ah, **Bonjour mes petit pois**. My apologies for my late arrival but I **bumpity-bumped** into CRUEL CROMWELL and had to hotfoot it. Not so easy, as you can see,' Lully said, pointing to the plaster around his foot.

'Who is Cruel Cromwell?' the children asked Peri.

'With any luck, you won't find out, but he dislikes anything that might be fun,' said the professore. 'Let's not dwell on Cromwell for now. This is my friend **Monsieur Luckless Lully**, he is the **father of French opera.**'

'**Et aussi, Superintendent of the Royal Music and the Music Master of the Royal Family!**' Lully added.

'Wow, that sounds posh,' Megan smiled. She was very impressed.

'**Oui...**' confirmed Lully, mopping his brow.

'I could do with a *wee* actually,' said Jack.

'Jack, shh! **Oui** is French for yes,' whispered Megan.

'Ohh,' Jack said sheepishly.

Monsieur – French for 'mister'. Quel désastre – 'what a disaster' in French.
Mon Dieu – how the French say 'my God!'. Bonjour – French for 'good morning'.
Mes petit pois – French for 'my green peas'. Et aussi – 'and also' in French. Oui – 'yes' in French.

Lully continued, 'I will say zis only once. I 'ad an accident beyond accidents... **_Regardez!_**' Luckless Lully pointed to his leg. 'See, I hit *mon* foot with ze DEMON BEATING STICK while I was conducting. **_Un, deux, trois,_** OOOWWW!' he screamed, hitting his foot again. 'I died an 'orrible death while working for **King Louis XIV of France.**'

'AH, you're French?' confirmed Jack.

'French, my foot,' quipped Trunk.

'**SHUT UP.** I was Italian, but I became French 'cause I prefer croissants to pizza...'

Suddenly, it dawned on Jack and Megan that perhaps all the Academy were... **DEAD!!**

Baroque composers like Lully hit the ground with a big wooden stick called a beating stick to set the pace the orchestra should play at. Lully injured his foot doing just this and it led to a nasty end when the wound became infected. The beating stick was replaced in 1820 by the baton you see a conductor using today.

Regardez – 'look' in French. *Un*, *deux*, *trois* – 'one, two, three' in French.

King Louis XIV of France (1638-1715) was king for 72 years, the longest ruling monarch in history! He was commonly known as the Sun King.

CHAPTER 10
Will Opera Live Forever?

'Professore, can I ask you a question please?' whispered Megan.

'*Sì*, of course.'

'Are you all...umm...' Megan searched for the right word.

'Composers? *Sì*.'

'No...are you all...err...' Megan paused again, but before she could finish Jack shouted, **'Decomposing?** Are you all DEAD?'

Peri rolled his eyes. Now, how do I explain this, he thought.

'What we do here at **the Academy** with our music and stories touches the hearts and souls of people all around the world, and that keeps us all alive,' Peri told them. 'If our work is ever FORGOTTEN, then it could disappear forever.'

'Gran says that about her old stories. She needs to share them with us so we'll always remember her when she has gone to the stars,' said Jack.

'What a lovely, wise gran you have. Remember her words, Jack.'

Maestro Monte piped up, 'I was nearly forgotten last year, but luckily somebody played my music in **SCRATCHY BOTTOM.**'

Jack giggled. 'Can you get cream for that?'

'If you hadn't found me in the old music hall, I think I might have been forgotten and disappeared too,' Trunk told the children.

'I'm so glad we found you, Trunk, and that you brought us to the Academy to meet everyone,' said Megan.

Scratchy Bottom **REALLY** is a village in Dorset, England. Imagine having to tell anyone where you come from...

As the children began to understand the situation, they were interrupted by the sound of marching footsteps.

'Oh no, it's HIM!' cried Lully.

CHAPTER 11
Cruel Cromwell

All of a sudden the Academy's doors burst open, and in stormed an army of soldiers dressed in flame-red uniforms with helmets that looked like upside-down saucepans.

'Pray silence for Lord Protector Cromwell,' announced the head soldier. As the name **'Cromwell'** resonated around the Academy, all the happiness and music the children had shared with their new friends seemed to disappear. Even the fiery Maestro Monte didn't want to face the **Dark Lord Protector.**

In a sudden panic, Monte pushed Jack and Megan forward, face to face with the largest crop of pimples they had ever seen, and breath so strong it was dangerous.

'Who are you?' stuttered Jack.

'Oliver Cromwell, Lord Protector of the Commonwealth to you. I ban all enjoyable things,' sneered the pimple-faced man.

'That's so cruel,' said Jack nervously.

'Yep, you've got me,' hissed the Dark Lord.

'Even music?' asked Megan sheepishly.

'Yes. All gone. Music is sinful. What I want is **work, work, work,** so that means all of you can **stop composing** and do something useful, you bunch of barmy **NINCOMPOOPS.** You'll be forgotten forever, if I have my way!' Cromwell's voice boomed like thunder across the Academy.

Jack knew just what bullies could be like, he'd been bullied before at school, but he wasn't about to allow his new friends to be bullied too. He mustered up his courage, 'You're a real bully! My school doesn't allow bullying, and neither does the Academy.'

Cruel Oliver Cromwell
1599-1658

A brilliant military leader, Member of Parliament and Lord Protector of the Commonwealth of England, Scotland and Ireland from 1653-1658. Cromwell was a very religious man and known as a Puritan. He banned many things, including sport, kissing, hot food on a Sunday, theatre, and Halloween.

Cromwell helped have King Charles I beheaded for his crimes in 1649. Cromwell himself was buried in Westminster Abbey but his corpse was dug up, hung in chains and beheaded by the new king Charles II, the party king.

'What?!' Cromwell span around and stared at Jack. 'Be careful, sonny Jim, I've chopped a king's head off in the past,' he sneered.

Jack worried about his own head, but Megan wasn't going to be bullied by anyone.

'Hold on a minute, **Old Ironsides***, if it's work you want, what about opera?' she challenged.

'Opera? **What is this OPERA?**' Cromwell demanded.

'It means work,' said Jack, his courage growing again.

'To work really, really hard,' Megan chipped-in further.

Cromwell thought about this. 'Hmmm... Work, you say?'

'My friends here at the Academy **invented** it, and it's brilliant,' said Jack.

Cromwell mulled this information over.

'So, do you all do this **opera thing?**' he asked.

'*Sì, yes, oui, ja,*' the composers all replied.

Cromwell grabbed Megan. 'Now listen, missy... Does **opera** really mean **work?**'

Megan nodded nervously, followed by Jack and the rest of the Academy.

'All right, **BLOCKHEADS** – I've got a deal for you. Come to my palace and show me one of your operas. If I like it, I might just keep it! Must dash – I have so many people to upset today.'

Oliver Cromwell lived at **Hampton Court**, near London. It is one of only two palaces once owned by King Henry VIII still standing. I bet that building has some amazing stories – they'd certainly make for a scary opera.

*The 'Ironsides' were the army formed by Oliver Cromwell during the English Civil War (1642-1651). 'Old Ironsides' became one of Cromwell's nicknames.
'Blockhead' was a word invented in 1549 for someone who was stupid! King Charles I became quite the blockhead when Cromwell had him executed!

As his soldiers marched out of the Academy, Cromwell turned, laughing loudly, and shouted back at the children.

'By the way, **I'm banning Christmas... HO, HO, HO.'**

'What a meanie,' Jack said.

'Don't worry, he won't get away with that,' said Trunk.

Cromwell banned everything that was fun. He ruled for 12 years and the only music he allowed was... Yes, you guessed it, **OPERA!**

Christmas was restored, along with the British monarchy, when King Charles II took the throne in 1660.

45

CHAPTER 12
The Opera Heroes!

Professor Peri, Maestro Monte, Fantastica Francesca, Perfect Purcell, Luckless Lully, Herr Handel, Doc Blow and all the other composers gathered around Jack and Megan, thankful for what they had done.

'You really are our heroes,' smiled Francesca, 'and it's all down to **the ABC.'**

'**The Academy of Barmy Composers!**' chorused the children.

'More than that,' Francesca replied, still smiling. '*A* – **Any**, *B* – **Body**, *C* – **Can**, when they believe in themselves!'

Megan and Jack smiled back, but Jack felt particularly proud for standing up to Cromwell. He knew that with Megan's help, they could do anything.

But their troubles weren't over yet – even if Cromwell loved their performance, it wouldn't keep the Academy going forever. With that, Peri waved his hand with one of his famous flourishes in celebration and a dust cloud flew from his arm… **PUFF!**

'Oh gosh, the professore and his music are beginning to fade!' Purcell gasped.

'Ah, I suppose I was always going to be one of the first to go,' Peri said, a little frightened.

'It's worse than I thought,' Trunk said to the children. The professore's music isn't *appreciated* – it's not **cool** in the modern day. Unless we do something soon, the whole Academy could go to the FORGOTTEN LAND. Not a place we want to go.'

'But we believe in the ABC!' the children said. 'What should we do?'

'SHARE OUR MUSIC!!!
TELL EVERYONE
ABOUT US!!!!!'
shouted the Academy.

CHAPTER 13
The Return

'Boss, there's no time to waste,' Trunk warned.

Francesca added, 'If Jack and Megan can stand up to **CROMWELL**, surely we stand a chance?'

'Sì, Francesca, I think you might be right,' considered the professore.

Peri turned to the children and asked, 'Jack and Megan, can you help us save the Academy and *opera?*'

'Yes, of course we will!'

'*Fantastici*, then you must leave immediately and tell everyone back home about us! Quickly, *adesso!* Trunk, *subito!'*

Trunk fired up his engines and lifted his lid for each of the **BAA-ROCKERS** to put something inside: **wigs, costumes, music** and **props** came from all directions to remind the children of their amazing adventure. The children so wanted to stay with their new friends, but now they had work to do.

Adesso – 'now' in Italian.
Subito – Italian for 'immediately' or 'straight away'.

'Look after them, Trunk, you have very important cargo there,' Professor Peri said, wiping away a little tear.

'Will do, Prof!' said Trunk.

'I promise we'll save you. I'm going to tell everyone that opera is amazing. My music teacher will love you,' Megan said.

'And my gran,' said Jack, bursting into **song:**

'Oppppeeerrraaaa!

What other music can compare?
We love your opera,
There's always magic in the air,
So just listen to the music,
And you'll find out of the blue,
That the A B C of opera's
For me, and you!'

Peri smiled again. 'I think you are a star in the making! Now go, my opera heroes. Travel well!'

Trunk shouted, '*ACCELERANDO*,' and **WHOOSH**, they were on their way.

Before you could say *Rocambolesco*, Trunk yelled, **'BRACE yourselves**,' as another risky landing propelled his contents, including the children, across the path of the music hall. 'I'll have to get my landings sorted – there are plenty more to come,' said a breathless Trunk.

'When will we see you again, Trunk?' the children asked, not wanting their time together to end.

'When you are ready, I will return and take you on another opera adventure – you have only scratched the surface. There's **CLASSICAL**, *Romantic* and **MODERN** all still to discover. But *Baroque (Baa-Rock)* is your challenge... Save their stories and music, like you saved me!'

Before the children could say their goodbyes, Trunk had already shot high into the air and vanished out of sight.

Rocambolesco:
An Italian word based on the swashbuckling hero Rocambole, star of a series of French novels by Pierre Alexis Ponson du Terrail, the first of which was published in 1857. Rocambole's name can be used to refer to fantastic adventures like this one.

Accelerando – 'with speed' in Italian.

CHAPTER 14
It's Just Beginning!

'Did that really happen? asked Megan, trying not to doubt their adventure, though it seemed impossible. 'We can't let them disappear, can we, Jack?'

'We won't, Megan. Remember the A B C, Any Body Can! **And we can, together!'**

As they walked back down their street, Jack noticed the wind was blowing a letter towards him. He reached out to catch it and saw it was addressed to them.

Cari amici,

By the time you read this letter you should be safely home, having survived another of Trunk's disastrous landings. The way you protected us against Cruel Cromwell leaves me with no doubt that you are the chosen ones who can save our music, stories and The Academy of Barmy Composers. We will miss you here.

Go, with kindness, my opera heroes.
Until we meet again...

Con affetto,

Professor Peri
Florence, 1633.

Cari amici – 'dear friends' in Italian.
Con affetto – 'with love' in Italian.

The Baroque Period (1597-1750)

The word Baroque comes from the Portuguese *Barroco*, referring to pearls that are oddly shaped. The Baroque period was full of inspirational people who dared to be 'ODD' and think outside the box, and they began expressing themselves in a bigger, more exciting way. The music of 'Busy Bach' and 'Herr Handel' sounded overly fussy compared to what people had heard before, but it soon became loved.

It wasn't just the music that was changing: philosophers like Isaac Newton, playwrights like William Shakespeare and astrologers like Galileo were seeing the world differently. Hans Lippershey invented the telescope, which made us see beyond our own planet, and amazing artists like Rembrandt helped us see art in a new way.

Famous people in the Baroque period that you should check out:

Mary Queen of Scots, William Shakespeare, Elizabeth I of England, Guy Fawkes, Mary I of England, Galileo Galilei, Anne Boleyn, Pocahontas, Oliver Cromwell, Edward VI of England, Shah Jahan, Catherine of Aragon, Phillip II of Spain, Walter Raleigh, Francis Bacon, Ivan the Terrible, Anne of Cleves, Catherine Parr, John Calvin, Hieronymus Bosch, Francis Xavier, Peter Paul Rubens and Sandro Botticelli.

Some instruments in a Baroque orchestra

Harpsichord A kind of piano with a more distinctive plucked sound, a bit like an old music box.

Organ A large piped instrument with pedals and a keyboard, similar to a piano. It has a very loud and impressive sound.

Woodwind: Recorders, flutes, oboes and bassoon The Baroque flutes were wooden. Modern flutes are metal.

String instruments: Violins, violas, cellos, viols and double basses: Viols look like violins but are held vertically instead of horizontally. Viols have 6 strings whereas violins have 4.

Lute: You might think the lute is a guitar, but it's more half-egg shaped. It has a long neck and you pluck the strings to play it like a harp.

Brass: Trumpet, horns. The baroque trumpet was called a natural trumpet and, unlike the modern-day trumpet, it had no valves.

Timpani: The big drums you can see at the back of the orchestra.

Voice Types

Opera singers are like Olympic athletes; they have to train their voices for years to sing as perfectly as possible and be heard over an orchestra without any microphone.

Soprano

The highest female voice (a soprano singing super-high notes can sometimes smash a glass). The soprano often sings the daughter or princess in an opera and usually dies at the end... Poor soprano.

Mezzo-soprano

This is a deeper voice than soprano. *Mezzo* means half in Italian, so mezzo-soprano must mean half a soprano – I wonder whether it's the top or bottom half? They usually play the cheeky girls, witches or even pretend to be boys... I told you opera was crazy!

Contralto

The lowest of the female voices, so low that it can sometimes sound like a burp. They often sing the parts of old grannies and maids and are usually very cuddly.

Countertenor

A countertenor is the highest male voice, so high that sometimes only my dog can hear it!

Tenor

A singing voice between baritone and countertenor. The most romantic of the male voices, in opera the tenor is often the young hero.

Baritone

Lower than a tenor (but not as low as a fiver, ha, ha). The baritone is the middle of the male voices. A baritone normally plays roles like the dad, brother, servant or even the villain with a big curly moustache.

Bass

The lowest, deepest male voice, so low and calming that it might put you to sleep. The bass is often the king, wizard or priest in an opera.

The Composers

Professor Peri
The Inventor of Opera
Full name: Jacopo Peri.
Nickname: *Il Zazzerino* or Golden Locks.
Nationality: Italian.
Born: Rome, Italy, 1561.
Buried: Florence, Italy, 1633.
Star Sign: Leo (the lion, also with a golden mane).
Jobs: Singer, actor, organist, composer.
Friends: *Camerata di Bardi* including Galileo (look him up).
Best friends: Jacopo Corsi & Count Giovanni de Bardi – top blokes.
Favourite food: Peri Peri Chicken.
Operas: *Dafne* (1598), *Euridice* (1600), *La Flora* (1628).
Role at the Academy: Top dog/ Headmaster.

Fantastica Francesca
First Female Opera Composer
Full name: Francesca Caccini.
Nickname: *La Cecchina* – The Songbird.
Nationality: Italian.
Born: Florence, Italy, 1587.
Buried: Florence, Italy, 1640.
Star Sign: Virgo (a strong, tough lady – *fantastica*).
Jobs: Singer, lutenist (someone who plays the lute), harpist, harpsichordist, theorbist, guitarist, poet, composer, music teacher.
Friends: The super rich and powerful Medici family.
Papà: Giulio Caccini (also a brilliant composer).
Operas: *La liberazione di Ruggiero dall'isola d'Alcina* (1625) – BIT OF A MOUTHFUL!
Role at the Academy: Girl Power.

Luckless Lully

The Papa of French Opera

Full name: Jean-Baptiste Lully in France and Giovanni Battista Lulli in Italy.

Nickname: Luckless, or *Quel Désastre.*

Nationality: Italian, French from 1661.

Born: Florence, Italy, 1632.

Buried: Paris, France, 1687.

Titles: Superintendent of the Royal Music and the Music Master of the Royal Family.

Star Sign: Scorpio (I wonder if he had a sting?).

Fun Fact: Lully died of gangrene in his foot caused by an injury from his long conducting stick (ouch, what a silly billy).

Jobs: Violinist, composer, dancer, director of the Académie Royale de Musique (posh).

Friends: Molière (one of the greatest French writers), King Louis XIV (the silly wigs are all down to him, as he was BALD).

Wife: Madeleine Lambert. (Her father, Michel Lambert, was a famous singer.)

Operas: From the classical *Atys* (1676) and *Isis* (1677) to the heroic *Roland* (1685) and the pastoral *Le Temple de la Paix* (1685).

Role at the Academy: Health and Safety.

Too Hot to Handel

Greatest German Composer

Full name: Georg Friedrich Händel.

Nationality: German, English.

Born: Halle an der Saale, Germany, 1685.

Buried: Westminster Abbey, London, 1759. Lots of them are buried there, so be careful if you visit.

Why does he look sad?: He worried and worried as he had so much music to compose.

Star Sign: Aquarius (same as Mozart, we might meet him next time).

Parents: Valentin Handel and Anna Belching, who were coppersmiths.

Jobs: Choir boy, composer, Director of Music at the Royal Academy of Music, *Kapellmeister* (person in charge of music) for George, Elector of Hanover. This 'George' became George I, King of England.

Friends: King George I.

Operas: 42, including *Music for the Royal Fireworks* (1749) when 12,000 people turned up to watch.

Role at the Academy: Caretaker.

Maestro Monte

Papà dell' Opera

Full name: Claudio Giovanni Antonio Monteverdi.

Nickname: Green Mountain or Grumpy Pants.

Nationality: Italian.

Born: Cremona, Italy, 1567.

Buried: Venice, Italy, 1643.

Star Sign: Taurus (the hot-blooded bull).

Jobs: Violin player, choirmaster, composer, Catholic priest.

Wife: Claudia Cattaneo.

Kids: 3 little green mountains: Massimilino, Francesco and Leonora.

Operas: *L'Orfeo* (1607), *L'Arianna* (1608), *Il ballo delle ingrate* (1608), *Il combattimento di Tancredi et Clorinda* (1624), *Il ritorno d'Ulisse in patria* (1639), *L'incoronazione di Poppea* (1642).

Movies: The Full Monteverdi.

Role at the Academy: Harmony and Development.

Doc Blow

First English Opera Composer

Full name: Doctor John Blow (he makes all the crotchets and quavers feel better and tells everyone to have a rest).

Nationality: English.

Born: Nottingham, 1649.

Buried: Westminster Abbey, London, 1708 (under the organ).

Star Sign: Pisces (bet he's a good swimmer).

Jobs: Organist at Westminster Abbey, teacher, private musician for King James II, choirmaster at St Paul's Cathedral, composer.

Friends: Perfect Purcell and King Charles II (the king that brought back partying).

Wife: Elizabeth Braddock.

Kids: 4.

Tidy titles: Composer for the Chapel Royal and Master of the Children.

Opera: *Venus and Adonis* (1683).

Role at the Academy: Welfare Officer.

Perfect Purcell

The Greatest English Opera Composer for 3 Centuries

Full name: Henry Purcell.

Nickname: Piggy (the old Norman French word *pourcel* means 'PIGLET').

Nationality: English.

Born: Westminster, London, 1659.

Buried: Westminster Abbey, London, 1695.

Star Sign: Leo (he looks like a lion).

Jobs: Organist at Westminster Abbey, composer.

Food: Sunday roast dinner.

Family: Mum, dad and 2 brothers, who were all AMAZING musicians and filthy RICH.

Fact: By age 11, Purcell had written a song for King Charles II. In fact, he started composing at age 9, but sadly died at 36.

Suspicious death: Either a nasty chill or an overdose of chocolate (so be careful).

Operas: *Dido and Aeneas* (1688), *Dioclesian* (1690), *King Arthur* (1691), *The Fairy-Queen* (1692) and *Timon of Athens* (1695).

Role at the Academy: Chocolatier.

Other Baroque Composers

Arcangelo Corelli (1653-1713)

The Italian composer Corelli was also a violinist and teacher of Herr 'Hugely-Talented' Handel. Although his music was loved, he refused to have it published during his lifetime. Corelli is buried at the Pantheon in Rome.

Antonio Vivaldi (1678-1741)

Venetian virtuoso Vivaldi composed over 500 concertos, as well as being an ordained priest, just like Maestro Monte. His nickname was *Il Prete Rosso* (The Red Priest) because of his red hair. He made a lot of money but spent it all and died penniless. Oh yes, he was also asthmatic!

Girolamo Frescobaldi (1583-1643)

The fabulous Frescobaldi was very important at the Medici court in Florence. (Despite his name, he had all his own hair. 'BALDI', HA, HA, GET IT?)

Alessandro Scarlatti (1660-1725)

Scarlatti wrote over 100 operas, 600 cantatas and oratorios (a bit like an opera but you keep still when singing, no acting, no dancing). His sister was an opera singer.

Domenico Scarlatti (1685-1757)

The sixth son of Alessandro Scarlatti, Domenico Scarlatti was great friends with Herr Handel and a crazy composer in his own right.

Giovanni Battista Pergolesi (1710-1736)

Pergolesi and Alessandro Scarlatti started a new kind of opera – *opera buffa* – silly and funny operas that became really popular (everyone loves a laugh). As well as operas, Pergolesi also composed religious music – check out his *Stabat Mater*.

François Couperin (1668-1733)

French François was known as *Couperin le Grand* (Couperin the Great). There were many talented musicians in his family, but he really stood out.

Marc-Antoine Charpentier (1643-1704)

King Louis XIV liked Charpentier's music so much that he granted him a pension (money) in 1683, which was unheard of back then!

Jean-Philippe Rameau (1683-1764)

Born in Dijon – yes, where the mustard comes from! When Rameau died, over 1,500 people attended his funeral, with over 180 musicians performing... Phew, bet that was a long funeral.

Johann Sebastian Bach (1685-1750)

The German genius Bach was a very busy boy. He came from an incredibly musical family, wrote over 1,000 compositions and, believe it or not, had 20 kids.

Georg Philipp Telemann (1681-1767)

Georg composed over 601 pieces of music and played 10 instruments. Go Georg, the one man band!

Michael Praetorius (1571-1621)

A polyglot (someone who speaks a lot of languages), Praetorius was also a great organist and a pupil of Martin Luther, the professor of religion.

Johann Hermann Schein (1586-1630)

A German composer of the early Baroque period. He was one of the first to import the early Italian stylistic innovations into German music, and was one of the most polished composers of the period.

Samuel Scheidt (1587-1653)

A German composer, organist and teacher of the early Baroque period.

Heinrich Schütz (1585-1672)

Composer and organist, generally regarded as the most important German composer before Johann Sebastian Bach.

And there are loads more to discover!

Heroes and Accomplices

Jack

Age: 9.
Full name: Jack Lloyd Jones.
Nationality: Welsh/ Jamaican.
Born: Pontirgorffenol, 2009.
School: Pontirgorffenol Primary School, Yr 5.
Jobs: Student and Opera Hero.
Star Sign: Gemini.
BFF: Megan.
Favourite food: Gran's Caribbean chicken with rice.
Favourite hobbies: Football, rugby, rap music, and adventures with Megan.

Megan

Age: 10.
Full name: Megan Beatrice Evans.
Nationality: Welsh.
Born: Pontirgorffenol, 2009.
School: Pontirgorffenol Primary School, Yr 5.
Jobs: Student and Opera Hero.
Star Sign: Pisces.
BFF: Jack.
Favourite food: Dad's Sunday lunch.
Favourite hobbies: Reading, football, choir and adventures with Jack.

Gran

Age: 79.
Full name: Irie Cedella Jones.
Nationality: Jamaican.
Born: Stoney Hill, Jamaica, 1940.
Star Sign: Capricorn.
Favourite food: Spicy Jerk Chicken.
Favourite things: Cooking, storytelling, grandson Jack, son William (Jack's dad), family and friends.
BFF: Mrs Phillips at no. 7.
Husband: Jack Williams Jones, who sadly passed away.

Trunk

Age: 500+.
Full name: Trunk.
Nationality: International.
Born: Who knows?
Job: Time traveller.
BFFs: Composers all over the world, Jack and Megan.
Role at the Academy: The Keeper.

Questions & Answers

What is a composer?

The composer writes the music and brings the story to life.

What is a librettist?

A librettist writes the words that tell the story and these are sung with the composer's music.

What is the libretto?

The libretto is the words of the opera.

So what is an opera?

An opera is a story set to music. In the old days, operas were only really seen in palaces, but today you can see and hear opera in lots of places all over the world: theatres, TV, churches, schools, and loads more – keep an eye out. The singers tell the story from the stage and the orchestra plays in a lowered area at the front of the stage called a 'pit'.

What is an orchestra?

A group of musicians is called an orchestra and they accompany the singers on stage. The orchestra is led by the conductor. In the orchestra there are lots of different types of instruments including strings, woodwind, brass, and percussion.

What are opera songs called?

A song sung by one person in an opera is called an aria [ah-ree-ah]. It's an Italian word that means 'air', 'style' or 'manner'.

What is it called if two people sing together?

This is called a duet. 3 people performing together is a trio, 4 is a quartet, 5 is a quintet, 6 is a sextet, 7 is a septet and 8 is an octet.

What is an ensemble?

If more than two people sing together, that's an ensemble.

What's a chorus?

A chorus is a group of people singing together in an opera as part of the story – they are usually groups like soldiers, priests or nymphs. This can be really exciting and noisy.

What is an overture?

The overture is the music that plays at the beginning of the opera, before the main action takes place. In the old days, the overture was to shut everyone up!

What is the scenery?

The scenery can set the location and transport you to somewhere different and exciting. Costumes are the outfits worn by the singers and tell us about the character and the period of the opera.

The Story of Orpheus

The genius Ancient Greeks brought us theatre, geometry, the Olympics, a flushing toilet and fantastic stories that the opera dudes loved. Here's one...

Orpheus, our hero, possessed a super-duper power – Music! Whenever Orpheus sang or played his lute, everyone danced with joy, including the animals of the forest.

His music was so magical that he captured the heart of Eurydice, the most beautiful girl in the land. Everything was perfect for the happy couple, until one dark day when Eurydice was bitten by a poisonous snake and immediately died.

Orpheus was so broken-hearted that he journeyed to the underworld to rescue Eurydice.

On reaching the River Styx he was stopped by Charon the Ferryman and his three-headed dog, Cerberus. Orpheus began to sing and play his lute. Charon and Cerberus were so touched by Orpheus's music that they agreed to take him to see Pluto, the King of the Underworld, to plead for Eurydice's release.

Deeper and deeper into the underworld they travelled, where they found Eurydice being guarded by King Pluto himself.

At first, the King showed no pity, but when Orpheus started to sing, the beauty of his golden voice touched the heart of the king.

The king agreed to release Eurydice, on one condition – Orpheus could walk out of the Underworld with Eurydice following, but he was forbidden to look back at her or help her in any way until they arrived in the world of life and light. If for any reason he looked into her eyes, she would disappear forever.

The couple was almost free, when suddenly the overpowering sunlight blinded Orpheus and he foolishly turned around to look at Eurydice. In that split second, she vanished for good.

From that moment on, Orpheus was only able to sing of sadness, unable to bear life without his love, until the god Apollo eventually heard his pain.

Apollo offered Orpheus a choice: Either stay living on earth without Eurydice, or join her in the stars.

Orpheus made his choice, and so Apollo took him from earth to reunite with Eurydice in the heavens.

Now that's a 2,500-year-old story that captured the imagination of composers like Peri and Monteverdi, and is still performed regularly today.

Now you have been there too...
The *A*cademy of *B* army *C* omposers.
We've had a chance to sing,
And we've met a few composers on the way.
It's up to Jack and Megan to pass their stories on,
There's a lot for them to tell you,
Or Peri could be gone!
Look out for Trunk's adventures, there's bound to be more soon,
Classical, Romantic, and tons of opera tunes...

Give us an A... *A*
Give us a B... *B*
Give us a C... *C*... **Sì... Sì... Sì...!!**
It's the *A B C*... The *A B C*
The *A B C of Opera*.